Here
Comes
Night

Second Printing 1966

HERE COMES NIGHT

by Miriam Schlein

pictures by Harvey Weiss

Albert Whitman and Company   Chicago

Fishing boats
sail in from the sea.

The sun is setting.

The cows come home to the barn.
Tinkle, cow bells.

The sun sinks lower.

Two horses walk down the road.
They're not pulling
the plow any more.
Time to rest.
No more plow.

The sun sinks lower.

It is quiet now, and everyone
is coming home from work.

Daddy comes home, too.
Home to you.

Lower, sun, lower.
Day is through.
Half light and half dark.
The sun is gone away.
It's time to rest.
The end of day.

But up in the air
an airplane flies by.

This is not its time to rest.
It must keep going.

The light in the lighthouse
shines big and bright.
This is not its time to rest.
It must warn ships at sea.

Darker. Darker.

The stars come out.

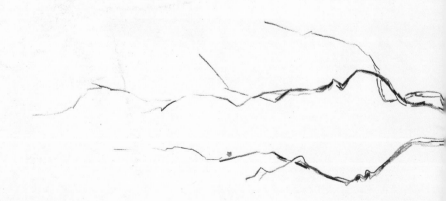

Darker. Darker.
Here comes night.

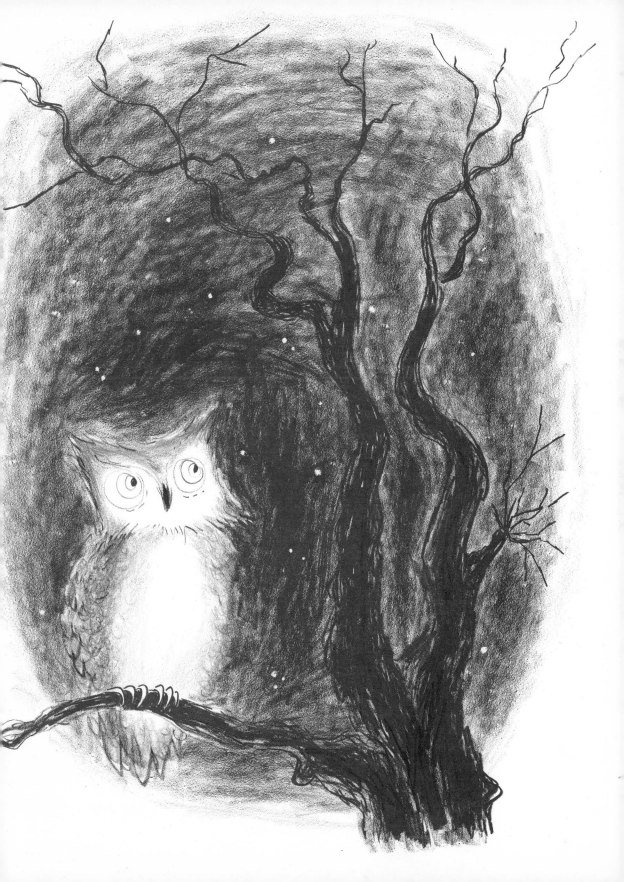

Silver moon hangs in the sky.
Waves go smack, smack.
Roll against the sand.
They never have a time to rest.
They never sleep at all.

The sea is dark.
The land is dark.
The horses, the cows,
the fishermen sleep.

You sleep.
I sleep.

Mother and Daddy sleep, sleep.
Work and play are for the day.
But night is dark for sleep.

SSSSHHH.

Quiet.

The world is very quiet.